Written Calculation
Multiplication 2
Answers

Introduction for parents and teachers

This book provides correct answers to all the questions in the Pupil Book **Written Calculation: Multiplication 2** (ISBN 978 07217 1269 7), including those contained in each **Check-up test** and **Final test**.

Which pupils will benefit most from Written Calculation: Multiplication 2?

Written Calculation covers multiplication in two books: pupils should work through both books consecutively to ensure that all the necessary steps are covered. **Multiplication 2** is for pupils who already understand the value of digits in numbers and have worked through **Multiplication 1**. They are able to identify the units digit in a four-digit number such as 5468. They also know the values of the other digits including tens, hundreds and thousands. Pupils should also be experienced in multiplying single-digit numbers (for example, 4 × 8, 8 × 3). Pupils who know by heart all their times tables will find written multiplication easier than those who have to work them out. For this reason, pupils who have not yet memorised their tables may find it useful temporarily to refer to a multiplication square – downloadable from the Schofield & Sims website. This will allow them to focus on the procedures of the written method. Once the pupils are familiar with the facts, they will no longer need the multiplication square.

How should the Pupil Book be used?

Pupils should work consecutively through all 18 'steps' if they are to become fully proficient in the most important stages of the learning process. At the end of each step are **Problem Solving** questions. Pupils record their workings onto the grids provided and also write their answers in the book. Make sure that each pupil completes the **self-evaluation** rating at the end of each step by ticking 'Easy', 'OK' or 'Difficult'. Review each pupil's rating against his or her score for that step, and give support to pupils who are struggling. The final steps in the book extend more able pupils and take them beyond the statutory aspects of written multiplication, requiring them to work with larger numbers and decimals, for example. **Check-up tests** and a **Final test** help you to monitor progress, and this book of **Answers** makes marking simple and quick. Use the **conversion chart** at the end of each test to quickly convert the pupil's score to a percentage that can be recorded and used to measure progress.

Please note: Pupils will require additional squared paper to help them complete some of the pages in the Pupil Book.

The separate **Written Calculation: Teacher's Guide** (ISBN 978 07217 1278 9) contains full teaching notes and assessment resources. The **Teacher's Resource Book** (ISBN 978 07217 1300 7) contains photocopiable resources. Both cover the whole series and provide the teacher with valuable guidance and resources to support the teaching of written calculation. For free downloads and for further details on all the other **Written Calculation** books, visit **www.schofieldandsims.co.uk**

Published by Schofield & Sims Ltd, Dogley Mill, Fenay Bridge, Huddersfield HD8 0NQ, UK Tel 01484 607080 www.schofieldandsims.co.uk

First published in 2015. Copyright © Schofield & Sims Ltd, 2015.

Authors: **Hilary Koll and Steve Mills**

Hilary Koll and Steve Mills have asserted their moral rights under the Copyright, Designs and Patents Act, 1988, to be identified as the authors of this work.

British Library Cataloguing in Publication Data

A catalogue record for this book is available from the British Library.

All rights reserved. No part of this publication may be reproduced, stored in a retrieval system, or transmitted in any form or by any means, electronic, mechanical, photocopying, recording or otherwise, without either the prior permission of the publisher or a licence permitting restricted copying in the United Kingdom issued by the Copyright Licensing Agency Limited, Saffron House, 6–10 Kirby Street, London EC1N 8TS.

Commissioned by **Carolyn Richardson Publishing Services (www.publiserve.co.uk)**

Design by **Ledgard Jepson Ltd**

Cover illustration by **Joe Hance (joehance.co.uk)**

Printed in the UK by **Wyndeham Gait Ltd, Grimsby, Lincolnshire**

ISBN 978 07217 1275 8

Contents

Step 1: Three- and four-digit × one-digit

In **Multiplication 1** you learnt how to multiply by one-digit numbers, such as 847×7. In this book you will learn how to do **long multiplication**, where you multiply by two-, three- or four-digit numbers. First we will revise one-digit multiplication.

What to do (a reminder)

$847 \times 7 = ?$

	TTh	Th	H	T	U
			8	4	7
×					7
					9
				4	

1 Multiply the digits of the top number, working from right to left. If you get more than 9 in any multiplication, carry sets of ten over to the column to the left. $7 \times 7 = 49$ so write 9 in the units column and carry the 4 tens over. Write the carried tens below the line.

			8	4	7
×					7
				2	9
			3	4	

2 Then multiply the tens digit, adding any carried tens. 4 tens × 7 = 28 tens, 28 tens + 4 carried tens = 32 tens. Write 2 in the tens column and carry the 3 hundreds.

			8	4	7
×					7
	5	9	2	9
	5	3	4	

3 Then multiply the hundreds digit, adding the carried hundreds. 8 hundreds × 7 = 56 hundreds. 56 hundreds + 3 carried hundreds = 59 hundreds. Write 9 in the hundreds column and carry the 5 thousands.

4 As the top number has no thousands you have no more multiplying to do, but you must write any carried thousands digits above the line to complete your answer.

Now you try

1

	9	1	4	8
×				5
4	5	7	4	0
4		2	4	

2

		3	9	6
×				8
	3	1	6	8
	3	7	4	

3

		7	6	1
×				6
	4	5	6	6
		4	3	

4

		2	9	8	7
×					4
	1	1	9	4	8
	1	3	3	2	

More practice   Set out these questions yourself to answer them.

5 6273 × 8 = ?

TTh	Th	H	T	U
	6	2	7	3
×				8
5	0	1	8	4
	5	2	5	2

6 1924 × 7 = ?

TTh	Th	H	T	U
	1	9	2	4
×				7
1	3	4	6	8
	1	6	1	2

7 4178 × 5 = ?

	4	1	7	8
×				5
2	0	8	9	0
	2		3	4

8 4557 × 9 = ?

	4	5	5	7
×				9
4	1	0	1	3
	4	5	5	6

Problem solving

9 Three people each win £1896 on the lottery. How much did they win altogether?

	1	8	9	6
×				3
5	6	8	8	
	2	2	1	

£5688

10 Every day 8925 people travel on a train. How many people travel on this train in a week?

	8	9	2	5
×				7
6	2	4	7	5
6	6	1	3	

62 475

11 Work out the missing digit in this multiplication.

	6	(7)	8	4
×				8
5	4	2	7	2
5	6	6	3	

Step 2: Two-, three- and four-digit ×10 and ×20

TTh	Th	H	T	U
	3	4	7	9
×			1	0
3	4	7	9	**0**

Now you need to remind yourself how to multiply by 10 and 20. When multiplying by 10 the digits of the number being multiplied move one place to the left. We put a zero into the units column to complete the answer.

What to do (a reminder)

$3479 \times 20 = ?$

1 To multiply by 20, first write zero in the units column.

	TTh	Th	H	T	U
		3	4	7	9
×				2	0
				8	**0**

2 Then multiply the top number by 2, but writing the digits of the answer one place to the left. Start by multiplying the units digit by 2: $9 \times 2 = 18$. Write the 8 and carry 1 across.

3 Now multiply the tens digit and add the carried digit.

4 Then multiply the hundreds digit and add any carried digits.

		3	4	7	9
×				2	0
	6	9	5	8	**0**

5 Finally, multiply the thousands digit and add any carried digits.

Now you try

1

	3	1	8
×		1	0
3	1	8	**0**

2

	1	7	8	7
×			2	0
3	5	7	4	**0**

3

	4	8	3	6
×			1	0
4	8	3	6	**0**

4

	5	6	8	9
×			2	0
1	1	3	7	8	**0**

More practice

5

		7	7	7	7
×				2	0
1	5	5	5	4	0

6

		9	6	8	9
×				1	0
	9	6	8	9	0

Set out these questions yourself to answer them.

7 4762 × 10 = ?

HTh	TTh	Th	H	T	U
		4	7	6	2
×				1	0
	4	7	6	2	0

8 9569 × 20 = ?

HTh	TTh	Th	H	T	U
		9	5	6	9
×				2	0
1	9	1	3	8	0

Problem solving

9 How many times greater is the answer to 635 × 20 than the answer to 127 × 10?

```
        6  3  5              1  2  7
   ×       2  0         ×       1  0
  1  2  7  0  0        1  2  7  0
```

12700 is 10 times greater than 1270

10 A row of terraced houses is made from 20 joined houses, each identical in size. If the width of each house is 486cm, what is the width of the terrace?

```
      4  8  6
   ×     2  0
   9  7  2  0
```

9720cm
or 97.2m

11 Use the digits 6, 7, 8 and 9 in any order to make a four-digit number. Multiply the number by 20. Can you find the number that gives the answer 173940? Use spare paper for working.

```
      8  6  9  7
   ×        2  0
  1  7  3  9  4  0
```

8697

| How did I find Step 2? | ☐ Easy | ☐ OK | ☐ Difficult |

Step 3: Two- and three-digit × a teens number
no carrying in the addition

Now you should be feeling confident enough to put it all together and multiply by a 'teens' number.

	H	T	U
	2	0	4
×		1	3

What to do

$204 \times 13 = ?$

1 In the first row under the question multiply the top number by the **units** digit of the bottom number: 204 × 3. Remember to work from right to left and carry if necessary. It helps to make your carry numbers quite small if you can.

Th	H	T	U	
	2	0	4	
×		1	3	
	6	1₁	2	← 204 × 3
2	0	4	0	← 204 × 10

2 In the next row multiply the top number by 10. Simply write a zero in the units column first and multiply the top number by 1, writing the digits one place to the left. 204 × 10 = 2040

3 Finally add your two answers. Be careful **not** to add the carry marks you used when multiplying. Just add the digits of the two answers.
612 + 2040 = 2652

		2	0	4	
	×		1	3	
		6	1₁	2	← 204 × 3
+	2	0	4	0	← 204 × 10
	2	6	5	2	

Now you try

1

		1	3	2	
	×		1	4	
		5₁	2	8	← 132 × 4
+	1	3	2	0	← 132 × 10
	1	8	4	8	

2

		1	3	1	
	×		1	5	
		6₁	5	5	← 131 × 5
+	1	3	1	0	← 131 × 10
	1	9	6	5	

3

		2	1	5	
	×		1	3	
		6	4₁	5	← 215 × 3
+	2	1	5	0	← 215 × 10
	2	7	9	5	

4

		2	1	1	
	×		1	4	
		8	4	4	← 211 × 4
+	2	1	1	0	← 211 × 10
	2	9	5	4	

More practice

5

		1	0	6
	×		1	6
		6	3₃	6	← 106 × 6
+	1	0	6	0	← 106 × 10
	1	6	9	6

6

		5	3	4
	×		1	4
	2₂	1₁	3₁	6	← 534 × 4
+	5	3	4	0	← 534 × 10
	7	4	7	6

7

		3	0	7
	×		1	3
		9	2₂	1	← 307 × 3
+	3	0	7	0	← 307 × 10
	3	9	9	1

8

		2	3	4
	×		1	7
	1₁	6₂	3₂	8	← 234 × 7
+	2	3	4	0	← 234 × 10
	3	9	7	8

Set out these questions yourself to answer them.

q 43 × 15 = ?

Th	H	T	U
		4	3
×		1	5
	2₂	1₁	5
+	4	3	0
	6	4	5

10 214 × 13 = ?

Th	H	T	U
	2	1	4
×		1	3
	6	4₁	2
+	2	1	4	0
	2	7	8	2

Problem solving

11 Twelve people each win £214 on the lottery. How much did they win altogether?

		2	1	4
	×		1	2
		4	2	8
+	2	1	4	0
	2	5	6	8

£2568

How did I find Step 3?	☐ Easy	☐ OK	☐ Difficult

Step 4: Two- and three-digit × a teens number with carrying in the addition

These are similar to Step 3 but, when you add your two answers at the final stage, you might need to do some carrying.

	H	T	U
	2	5	1
×		1	3

What to do

$251 \times 13 = ?$

1 First multiply the top number by the units digit of the bottom number: 251 × 3. Remember to work from right to left and carry if necessary.

2 In the next row multiply the top number by 10. Simply write a zero in the units column first and multiply the top number by 1, writing the digits one place to the left. 251 × 10 = 2510

3 Finally add your two answers. Be careful not to add the carry marks you used when multiplying. Just add the digits of the two answers. You might need to carry when adding. Here 7 hundreds + 5 hundreds = 12 hundreds, so carry 1 thousand. 753 + 2510 = 3263

Th	H	T	U	
	2	5	1	
×		1	3	
	7₁	5	3	← 251 × 3
2	5	1	0	← 251 × 10

	H	T	U	
	2	5	1	
×		1	3	
	7₁	5	3	
+ 2	5	1	0	
3	2	6	3	

Now you try

1

		6	3	
×		1	3	
	1₁	8	9	← 63 × 3
+	6	3	0	← 63 × 10
	8	1	9	

2

		1	8	4	
	×		1	7	
	1₁	2₅	8₂	8	← 184 × 7
+	1	8	4	0	← 184 × 10
	3	1	2	8	

3

		3	5	2	
	×		1	5	
	1₁	7₂	6₁	0	← 352 × 5
+	3	5	2	0	← 352 × 10
	5	2	8	0	

4

		4	5	6	
	×		1	4	
	1₁	8₂	2₂	4	← 456 × 4
+	4	5	6	0	← 456 × 10
	6	3	8	4	

More practice

5

		1	9	6	
×			1	6	
1	1₁	1₅	7₃	6	← 196 × 6
+	1	9	6	0	← 196 × 10
	3	1	3	6	

6

		3	6	4	
×			1	8	
	2₂	9₅	1₃	2	← 364 × 8
+	3	6	4	0	← 364 × 10
	6	5	5	2	

Set out these questions yourself to answer them.

7 44 × 19 = ?

Th	H	T	U
		4	4
×		1	9
	3₃	9₃	6
+		4	4	0
		8	3	6

8 658 × 13 = ?

Th	H	T	U
	6	5	8
×		1	3
1₁	9₁	7₂	4
+	6	5	8	0
	8	5	5	4

Problem solving

9 Answer each of these multiplications using the same method.

111 × 19 = __2109__

222 × 19 = __4218__

333 × 19 = __6327__

```
      1 1 1          2 2 2          3 3 3
  ×     1 9      ×     1 9      ×     1 9
      9 9 9      1₁9₁9₁8      2₂9₂9₂7
  + 1 1 1 0      + 2 2 2 0      + 3 3 3 0
    2 1 0 9        4 2 1 8        6 3 2 7
```

Then look for patterns in the digits of the answers.
Can you use what you notice to predict the answer of 444 × 19?   __8436__

| How did I find Step 4? | ☐ Easy | ☐ OK | ☐ Difficult |

Step 5: Three-digit × a teens number five-digit answers

Try these in the same way. Some of your answers may be five-digit numbers.

What to do

$986 \times 13 = ?$

1 First multiply the top number by the units digit of the bottom number. $986 \times 3 = 2958$

2 In the next row multiply the top number by 10. Remember to write a zero in the units column first. $986 \times 10 = 9860$

TTh	Th	H	T	U	
		9	8	6	
	×		1	3	
	2$_2$	9$_2$	5$_1$	8	← 986 × 3
	9	8	6	**0**	← 986 × 10

3 Finally add your two answers. Be careful not to add the carry marks you used when multiplying. Just add the digits of the two answers. You might need to carry when adding.

		9	8	6
	×		1	3
	2$_2$	9$_2$	5$_1$	8
+		9	8	6	**0**
	1	2	8	1	8

Now you try

1

		9	7	3	
	×		1	5	
	4$_4$	8$_3$	6$_1$	5	← 973 × 5
+	9	7	3	**0**	← 973 × 10
1	4	5	9	5	

2

		5	7	6	
	×		1	9	
	5$_5$	1$_6$	8$_5$	4	← 576 × 9
+	5	7	6	**0**	← 576 × 10
1	0	9	4	4	

3

		8	6	9	
	×		1	4	
	3$_3$	4$_2$	7$_3$	6	← 869 × 4
+	8	6	9	0	← 869 × 10
1	2	1	6	6	

4

		9	5	8	
	×		1	8	
	7$_7$	6$_4$	6$_6$	4	← 958 × 8
+	9	5	8	0	← 958 × 10
1	7	2	4	4	

More practice

Each of these questions has two missing digits. Can you work out which are missing?

5

```
        7  ③  4
    ×      1  6
   4₄ 4₂ 0₂ 4
 +  7  ③  4  0
 1  1  7  4  4
    1
```

6

```
       ⑧  2  5
    ×     1  7
   5₅ 7₁ 7₃ 5
 + ⑧  2  5  0
 1  4  0  2  5
    1  1  1
```

Problem solving

Use the same method to answer these questions.

7 124 teams entered the Schools' Rugby Cup. Each team has 15 players. How many players were involved?

```
      1  2  4
   ×     1  5
      6₁ 2₂ 0
 +  1  2  4  0
 1  8  6  0        1860
```

8 A mobile phone package charges 19p for each minute used. How much does it cost for 689 minutes of calls?

```
      6  8  9
   ×     1  9
     6₆ 2₈ 0₈ 1
 +  6  8  9  0          1309lp or
 1  3  0  9  1          £130.91
    1  1
```

9 A word-processing program puts 372 words on each page. How many words will be on 17 pages?

```
      3  7  2
   ×     1  7
    2₂ 6₅ 0₁ 4
 +  3  7  2  0
 6  3  2  4         6324
    1
```

10 At a garden centre a machine puts 654 seeds in each packet. How many seeds will be in 18 packets?

```
      6  5  4
   ×     1  8
    5₅ 2₄ 3₃ 2
 +  6  5  4  0
 1  1  7  7  2       11772
    1
```

Check-up test 1 Up to four-digit × one-digit, ×10, ×20, and × teen numbers

Step 1

1

	2	9	8	7
×				5
1	4	9	3	5
	1	4	4	3

2 $4127 \times 8 = ?$

	4	1	2	7
×				8
3	3	0	1	6
	3	1	2	5

Step 2

3

	6	3	2	8
×			1	0
6	3	2	8	0

4 $6789 \times 20 = ?$

		6	7	8	9
×				2	0
1	3	5	7	8	0
	1	1	1	1	

Steps 3 and 4

5 $329 \times 17 = ?$

		3	2	9
	×		1	7
	2_2	3_2	0_6	3
+	3	2	9	0
	5	5	9	3

6

		1	3	8
	×		1	6
	8_2	2_4	8	
+	1	3	8	0
	2	2	0	8
		1	1	

Step 5

7

			7	3	4
		×		1	5
		3_3	6_1	7_2	0
+		7	3	4	0
	1	1	0	1	0
			1	1	1

8

			8	8	8
		×		1	9
		7_7	9_7	9_7	2
+		8	8	8	0
	1	6	8	7	2
			1	1	1

Steps 1 to 5 mixed

Use the grid below for working.

9 Tins of beans weigh 443g each. How heavy are 12 tins of beans?

5316g or 5.316kg ☐ 9

10 A moped travels 13km for every litre of petrol. How far can it travel using 165 litres?

2145km ☐ 10

11 An author writes 14 pages every day. How many pages does she write in 731 days?

10 234 ☐ 11

12 A firm makes ladders. Each ladder has 16 rungs. How many rungs are needed to make 281 ladders?

4496 ☐ 12

```
9)        4  4  3
       ×     1  2
       ──────────
          8  8  6
    +  4  4  3  0
    ──────────────
       5  3  1  6
          ₁     ₁
```

```
10)          1  6  5
          ×     1  3
          ──────────
          4₁ 9₁ 5
       +  1  6  5  0
       ──────────────
          2  1  4  5
             ₁     ₁
```

```
11)       7  3  1
       ×     1  4
       ──────────
       2₂ 9₁ 2  4
    +  7  3  1  0
    ──────────────
    1  0  2  3  4
       ₁     ₁
```

```
12)          2  8  1
          ×     1  6
          ──────────
          1₁ 6₄ 8  6
       +  2  8  1  0
       ──────────────
          4  4  9  6
             ₁
```

Total test score

Score	1	2	3	4	5	6	7	8	9	10	11	12
%	8	17	25	33	42	50	58	67	75	83	92	100

☐ 12

Step 6: Three-digit × any two-digit multiple of 10

In Step 2 you practised multiplying by 10 or 20. Multiplying by 30, 40, 50 or any other two-digit multiple of 10 is just as easy!

What to do (a reminder)

$746 \times 40 = ?$

1 As you are multiplying by a multiple of 10, first write zero in the units column.

	TTh	Th	H	T	U
			7	4	6
×				4	0
				4	**0**
				2	

2 Then multiply the three-digit number by the other digit of the multiple of 10, which is 4 here. Write the digits of the answer one place to the left. Start with the units as before: $6 \times 4 = 24$. Carry 2 across and write the 4.

3 Now multiply the tens digit and add the carried digit.

4 Then multiply the hundreds digit, add the carried digit and complete your answer.

			7	4	6
×				4	0
	2	9	8	4	**0**
	2	1	2		

Now you try

1

		3	7	8
×			4	0
1	5	1	2	**0**
1	3	3		

2

		8	2	5
×			9	0
7	4	2	5	**0**
7	2	4		

3

		9	6	7
×			3	0
2	9	0	1	**0**
2	2	2		

4

		6	8	4
×			8	0
5	4	7	2	**0**
5	6	3		

More practice

5

		6	3	2
×			6	0
3	7	9	2	0
3	1	1		

6

		7	6	1
×			7	0
5	3	2	7	0
5	4			

Set out these questions yourself to answer them.

7 469 × 80 = ?

TTh	Th	H	T	U
		4	6	9
×			8	0
3	7	5	2	0
	3	5	7	

8 667 × 90 = ?

TTh	Th	H	T	U
		6	6	7
×			9	0
6	0	0	3	0
	6	6	6	

Problem solving

Circle 'true' or 'false' for each question.

9 564 × 30 has the same answer as 423 × 40.

```
      5  6  4              4  2  3
   ×     3  0           ×     4  0
   1  6  9  2  0        1  6  9  2  0    (true) / false
      1  1  1              1     1
```

10 363 × 80 has the same answer as 967 × 30.

```
      3  6  3              9  6  7
   ×     8  0           ×     3  0
   2  9  0  4  0        2  9  0  1  0    true / (false)
      2  5  2              2  2  2
```

11 456 × 90 has the same answer as 684 × 60.

```
      4  5  6              6  8  4
   ×     9  0           ×     6  0
   4  1  0  4  0        4  1  0  4  0    (true) / false
      4  5  5              4  5  2
```

12 448 × 70 has an answer that is 400 more than 516 × 60.

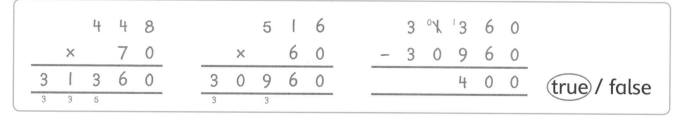

```
      4  4  8          5  1  6          3 ⁰₁ ¹3  6  0
   ×     7  0       ×     6  0       -  3  0  9  6  0
   3  1  3  6  0     3  0  9  6  0              4  0  0    (true) / false
      3  3  5           3     3
```

How did I find Step 6?   ☐ Easy   ☐ OK   ☐ Difficult

Step 7: Two- and three-digit × two-digit
no carrying in the addition

When multiplying by a two-digit number you multiply by the unit digit and the multiple of 10 separately. So, to multiply by 34, you multiply by 4 and then by 30 and then add the answers.

H	T	U
	1	1	4
×		3	4

(top-right working: H T U row shows 1 1 4; × row shows 3 4)

What to do

$114 × 34 = ?$

1   In the first row under the question multiply the top number by the units digit of the bottom number: $114 × 4$. Remember to work from right to left and to carry if necessary.

Th	H	T	U
		1	1	4
×			3	4
	4	5₁	6	← 114 × 4

2   In the next row multiply the top number by the multiple of 10. To multiply by 30, simply write a zero in the units column first and then multiply the top number by 3, carrying if necessary. $114 × 30 = 3420$

3   Finally add your two answers. Be careful not to add the carry marks you used when multiplying. Just add the digits of the two answers. $456 + 3420 = 3876$

		1	1	4
×			3	4
		4	5₁	6
+	3	4₁	2	0	← 114 × 30
	3	8	7	6

Now you try

1

			7	2
	×		6	3
		2₂	1	6	← 72 × 3
+	4₄	3₁	2	0	← 72 × 60
	4	5	3	6

2

			7	1
	×		5	6
		4₄	2	6	← 71 × 6
+	3₃	5	5	0	← 71 × 50
	3	9	7	6

3

			1	1	6
	×			2	3
			3	4₁	8	← 116 × 3
+		2	3₁	2	0	← 116 × 20
		2	6	6	8

4

			2	8	1
	×			3	5
		1₁	4₄	0	5	← 281 × 5
+		8₂	4	3	0	← 281 × 30
		9	8	3	5

More practice

5

		1	0	6
×			6	6
		6	3_3	6
+	6	3_3	6	0
	6	9	9	6

← 106 × 6
← 106 × 60

6

		2	3	4
×			3	8
1_1	8_2	7_3	2
+	7	0_1	2	0
	8	8	9	2

← 234 × 8
← 234 × 30

7

			6	7
×			3	9
		6_6	0_6	3
+	2_2	0_2	1	0
	2	6	1	3

← 67 × 9
← 67 × 30

8

			1	0	4
×				5	7
		7	2_2	8
+	5	2_2	0	0
	5	9	2	8

← 104 × 7
← 104 × 50

Set out these questions yourself to answer them.

9 71 × 66 = ?

Th	H	T	U
		7	1
×		6	6
	4_4	2	6
+	4_4	2	6	0
	4	6	8	6

10 203 × 43 = ?

Th	H	T	U
	2	0	3
×		4	3
	6	0	9
+	8	1_1	2	0
	8	7	2	9

Problem solving

11 If there are 52 weeks in every year, how many weeks are there in 28 years?

		5	2
×		2	8
	4_4	1_1	6
+	1_1	0	4	0
	1	4	5	6

1456 weeks

| How did I find Step 7? | Easy | OK | Difficult |

Step 8: Two- and three-digit × two-digit
with carrying in the addition

These are similar but, when you add your answers at the final stage, you might need to do some carrying.

What to do

$251 \times 36 = ?$

1 First multiply the top number by the units digit of the bottom number: 251×6. Remember to work from right to left and to carry if necessary.

Th	H	T	U
	2	5	1
×		3	6
1_1	5_3	0	6	← 251×6

2 In the next row multiply the top number by 30. Simply write a zero in the units column first and then multiply the top number by 3.
$251 \times 30 = 7530$

3 Finally add your two answers. Be careful not to add the carry marks you used when multiplying. Just add the digits of the two answers. But you might need to carry when adding. Here 5 hundreds + 5 hundreds = 10 hundreds so we carry 1 thousand.
$1506 + 7530 = 9036$

		2	5	1
	×		3	6
	1_1	5_3	0	6
+	7_1	5	3	0	← 251×30
	9	0	3	6

Now you try

1

		1	8	6
	×		4	4
		7_3	4_2	4	← 186×4
+	7_3	4_2	4	0	← 186×40
	8	1	8	4

2

			9	4
	×		5	7
		6_6	5_2	8	← 94×7
+	4_4	7_2	0	0	← 94×50
	5	3	5	8

3

		2	7	3
	×		3	6
	$1_{.1}$	6_4	3_1	8	← 273×6
+	8_2	1	9	0	← 273×30
	9	8	2	8

4

		1	3	8
	×		6	9
	1_1	2_3	4_7	2	← 138×9
+	8_2	2_4	8	0	← 138×60
	9	5	2	2

More practice

5

		1	2	6	
	×		7	6	
	7 $_1$	5 $_3$	6	← 126 × 6
+	8 $_1$	8 $_4$	2	0	← 126 × 70
	9	5	7	6	

6

		1	8	7	
	×		2	8	
	1 $_1$	4 $_6$	9 $_5$	6	← 187 × 8
+	3 $_1$	7 $_1$	4	0	← 187 × 10
	5	2	3	6	

Set out these questions yourself to answer them.

7 96 × 43 = ?

Th	H	T	U
		9	6
×		4	3
	2 $_2$	8 $_1$	8
+	3 $_3$	8 $_2$	4	0
4	1	2	8

8 159 × 53 = ?

Th	H	T	U
	1	5	9
×		5	3
	4 $_1$	7 $_2$	7
+	7 $_2$	9 $_4$	5	0
8	4	2	7

Problem solving

9 Answer each of these multiplications using this method.

11 × 99 = _1089_

22 × 99 = _2178_

33 × 99 = _3267_

			1	1				2	2				3	3
	×		9	9		×		9	9		×		9	9
			9	9			1 $_1$	9 $_8$	8			2 $_2$	9 $_2$	7
+		9	9	0	+	1 $_1$	9 $_8$	8	0	+	2 $_2$	9 $_2$	7	0
	1	0	8	9		2	1	7	8		3	2	6	7

Then look for patterns in the digits of the answers.
Can you use what you notice to predict the answer of 99 × 99? _9801_

Step 9: Three-digit × two-digit five-digit answers

Do these in the same way. Some of your answers may be five-digit numbers.

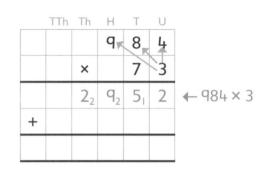

What to do

$984 \times 73 = ?$

1 First multiply the top number by the units digit of the bottom number. $984 \times 3 = 2952$

		TTh	Th	H	T	U	
				9	8	4	
	×				7	3	
			2_2	9_2	5_1	2	← 984 × 3
+							

2 In the next row multiply the top number by 70.
   $984 \times 70 = 68\,880$

3 Finally add your two answers. Be careful not to add the carry marks you used when multiplying. Just add the digits of the two answers.
   You might need to carry when adding.
   $2952 + 68\,880 = 71\,832$

				9	8	4
	×				7	3
			2_2	9_2	5_1	2
+		6_6	8_5	8_2	8	0	← 984 × 70
		7	1	8	3	2

Now you try

1

			7	4	2	
	×			6	6	
		4_4	4_2	5_1	2	← 742 × 6
+	4_4	4_2	5_1	2	0	← 742 × 60
	4	8	9	7	2	

2

			3	6	5	
	×			8	9	
		3_3	2_5	8_4	5	← 365 × 9
+	2_2	9_5	2_4	0	0	← 365 × 80
	3	2	4	8	5	

3

			8	7	3	
	×			3	4	
		3_3	4_2	9_1	2	← 873 × 4
+	2_2	6_2	1	9	0	← 873 × 30
	2	9	6	8	2	

4

			9	5	8	
	×			7	8	
		7_7	6_4	6_6	4	← 958 × 8
+	6_6	7_4	0_5	6	0	← 958 × 70
	7	4	7	2	4	

More practice

Each of these questions has a missing digit. Can you work out which digit is missing in each?

5

```
              5   7   6
      ×      (4)  6
      3₃  4₄  5₃  6
  +   2₂  3₃  0₂  4   0
      2   6   4   9   6
```

6

```
             (7)  1   7
      ×       8   9
      6₆  4₁  5₆  3
  +   5₅  7₁  3₅  6   0
      6   3   8   1   3
          |       |
```

Problem solving

7 Each box of pins contains 234 pins. How many pins will be in 76 boxes?

```
          2   3   4
      ×       7   6
      1₁  4₂  0₂  4
  +   1₁  6₂  3₂  8   0
      1   7   7   8   4      17784
```

8 What is 333 × 33?

```
          3   3   3
      ×       3   3
          9   9   9
  +       9   9   9   0
      1   0   9   8   9      10989
              |   |   |
```

9 Which is larger: 578 × 46 or 678 × 39?

```
          5   7   8                6   7   8
      ×       4   6            ×       3   9
      3₃  4₄  6₄  8            6₆  1₇  0₇  2
  +   2₂  3₃  1₃  2   0    +   2₂  0₂  3₂  4   0
      2   6   5   8   8        2   6   4   4   2
```

578 × 46, as 26588 is larger than 26442

How did I find Step 9?   ☐ Easy   ☐ OK   ☐ Difficult

Step 10: Four- and five-digit × two-digit

Now you can try to multiply larger numbers by two-digit numbers.

$$12\,504 \times 53 = ?$$

	HTh	TTh	Th	H	T	U	
			1	2	5	0	4
×						5	3
			3	7$_1$	5	1$_1$	2	← 12504 × 3
+							

What to do

1 First multiply the top number by the units digit of the bottom number, working from right to left as always. 12504 × 3 = 37512

2 In the next row multiply the top number by 50. 12504 × 50 = 625200

3 Finally add your two answers. Be careful not to add the carry marks you used when multiplying. Just add the digits of the two answers. You might need to carry when adding. 37512 + 625200 = 662712

		1	2	5	0	4	
	×				5	3	
		3	7$_1$	5	1$_1$	2	
+	6$_1$	2$_2$	5	2$_2$	0	**0**	← 12504 × 50
	6	6	2	7	1	2	
		1					

Now you try

1

			3	1	4	6	
	×				2	4	
		1$_1$	2	5$_1$	8$_2$	4	← 3146 × 4
+		6	2	9$_1$	2	**0**	← 3146 × 20
		7	5	5	0	4	
			1		1		

2

			7	2	8	3	
	×				7	5	
		3$_3$	6$_1$	4$_4$	1$_1$	5	← 7283 × 5
+	5$_5$	0$_1$	9$_5$	8$_2$	1	**0**	← 7283 × 70
	5	4	6	2	2	5	
			1		1		

3

		1	1	1	1	1	
	×				3	6	
		6	6	6	6	6	← 11111 × 6
+	3	3	3	3	3	**0**	← 11111 × 30
	3	9	9	9	9	6	

4

		1	5	1	8	9	
	×				6	2	
		3$_1$	0	3$_1$	7$_1$	8	← 15189 × 2
+	9$_3$	1$_1$	1$_5$	3$_5$	4	**0**	← 15189 × 60
	9	4	1	7	1	8	
			1				

More practice   Set out these questions yourself to answer them.

5 1546 × 88 = ?

	HTh	TTh	Th	H	T	U
			1	5	4	6
×					8	8
		1₁	2₄	3₃	6₄	8
+	1₁	2₄	3₃	6₄	8	0
	1	3	6	0	4	8

6 12 463 × 33 = ?

	HTh	TTh	Th	H	T	U
		1	2	4	6	3
×					3	3
		3	7₁	3₁	8	9
+	3	7₁	3₁	8	9	0
	4	1	1	2	7	9

Problem solving

7 Each letter stands for a digit in this multiplication.

Choose a digit to stand for the letter A, for example 2222 × 22 or 5555 × 55.

Find the answer and see if it matches the solution shown.

If not, using spare paper, try again with different digits.

Can you work out which digit the letter A stands for here?

			A	A	A	A
	×				A	A
		C	A	A	A	B
+	C	A	A	A	B	D
	A	C	A	A	D	B

A = 9

8 Peter earns £18 423 each year. How many years will it take him to earn over one million pounds? Will it take him 33 years, 55 years or 77 years?

	1	8	4	2	3
×				3	3
	5₂	5₁	2	6	9
+ 5₂	5₁	2	6	9	0
6	0	7	9	5	9

	1	8	4	2	3
×				5	5
	9₄	2₂	1₁	1₁	5
+ 9₄	2₂	1₁	1₁	5	0
1	0	1	3	2	6	5

55 years

How did I find Step 10?   ☐ Easy   ☐ OK   ☐ Difficult

Check-up test 2 Up to five-digit × two-digit

Step 6

1

		6	8	9
×			3	0
2	0	6	7	0
	2	2	2	

2 412 × 80 = ?

		4	1	2
×			8	0
3	2	9	6	0
	3		1	

Steps 7 and 8

3

		1	2	4
×			6	2
		2	4	8	← 124 × 2
+	7₁	4₂	4	0	← 124 × 60
	7	6	8	8

4 68 × 49 = ?

			6	8
×			4	9
		6₆	1₇	2	← 68 × 9
+		2₂	7₃	2	0	← 68 × 40
	3	3	3	2
	1			

Step 9

5

		8	9	7
×			5	7
	6₆	2₆	7₄	9
+	4₄	4₄	8₃	5	0
	5	1	1	2	9
	1	1	1	

6 638 × 36 = ?

			6	3	8
×				3	6
		3₃	8₂	2₄	8
+	1₁	9₁	1₂	4	0
	2	2	9	6	8
	1			

Step 10

7

	1	5	8	6	3
×				2	2
	3₁	1₁	7₁	2	6
+	3₁	1₁	7₁	2	6	0
3	4	8	9	8	6

8

	1	2	4	7	2
×				4	8
	9₁	9₃	7₅	7₁	6
+	4	9₁	8₂	8	8	0
5	9	8	6	5	6
	1	1	1	1	

□ 1
□ 2
□ 3
□ 4
□ 5
□ 6
□ 7
□ 8

Steps 6 to 10 mixed

Use the grid below for working.

9 Lily was paid £24 per day for one month (31 days). How much was she paid in total?

£744

☐ 9

10 A car travels 23km for every litre of petrol. How far can it travel using 175 litres?

4025km

☐ 10

11 Ajay worked for 246 days. He earns £56 per day. How much did he earn?

£13 776

☐ 11

12 A bicycle factory makes 67 wheels each day. How many wheels does it make in 365 days?

24 455

☐ 12

```
9)        2  4          10)            1  7  5
       ×  3  1                      ×     2  3
       ─────────                    ──────────────
          2  4                        5₁ 2₁ 5
    +  7₁ 2  0                    +  3₁ 5₁ 0  0
       ─────────                    ──────────────
       7  4  4                       4  0  2  5
                                            ₁


11)        2  4  6       12)            3  6  5
       ×      5  6                   ×        6  7
       ───────────────              ────────────────
       1₁ 4₂ 7₃ 6                    2₂ 5₄ 5₃ 5
    +  1₁ 2₂ 3₃ 0  0              +  2₂ 1₃ 9₃ 0  0
       ───────────────              ────────────────
       1  3  7  7  6                 2  4  4  5  5
                                             ₁
```

Total test score

Score	1	2	3	4	5	6	7	8	9	10	11	12
%	8	17	25	33	42	50	58	67	75	83	92	100

12

Step 11: Three-digit × three-digit multiples of 100

You learnt in Step 6 how to multiply by a multiple of 10. Here we'll look at multiplying by multiples of 100. They are just as easy!

H	T	U
9	7	1
× 5	0	0

What to do

$971 \times 500 = ?$

1 When multiplying by a multiple of 100, multiply first by 100. To make a number 100 times larger we move the digits of a number two places to the left. Write two zeros in the units and tens columns first to multiply by 100.

HTh	TTh	Th	H	T	U
			9	7	1
		× 5	0	0	
				0	0

2 Then just multiply the top number by the hundreds digit of the multiple of 100, which is 5 here. As always work from right to left and fill in the digits two places to the left.

HTh	TTh	Th	H	T	U
			9	7	1
		× 5	0	0	
4	8	5	5	0	0
	4	3			

Now you try

1

			8	2	5
		× 3	0	0	
2	4	7	5	0	0
	2		1		

2

			9	6	8
		× 4	0	0	
3	8	7	2	0	0
	3	2	3		

3

			6	6	6
		× 9	0	0	
5	9	9	4	0	0
5	5	5			

4

			3	4	7
		× 8	0	0	
2	7	7	6	0	0
2	3	5			

5

			5	7	6
		× 7	0	0	
4	0	3	2	0	0
4	5	4			

6

			8	0	6
		× 6	0	0	
4	8	3	6	0	0
4		3			

More practice

Each of these answers has an error. Write the error that has been made and give the correct answer.

7

		8	5	3
	×	7	0	0
5	9	7	1	0
	5	3	2	

Error: This is the answer to 853 × 70.

Correct answer: 597 100

8

		4	4	4
	×	9	0	0
3	9	6	6	0	0
3	3	3		

Error: One of the carried threes was not added on.

Correct answer: 399 600

Problem solving

9 A school receives £400 per pupil to pay for equipment. If there are 128 pupils at the school, how much does it receive altogether?

		1	2	8
	×	4	0	0
5	1	2	0	0
	1	3		

£51 200

10 Which is larger: 562 × 300 or 256 × 700?

		5	6	2
	×	3	0	0
1	6	8	6	0	0
	1	1		

		2	5	6
	×	7	0	0
1	7	9	2	0	0
	1	3	4	

256 × 700, as 168 600 is smaller than 179 200

11 There is a long fence around an airport. Each fence panel is 500cm wide. If there are 852 panels around the airport, what is the total length of the fence?

		8	5	2
	×	5	0	0
4	2	6	0	0	0
	4	2	1	

426 000cm or 4260m

12 Bags of flour weigh 800g. How heavy is 467 bags of flour altogether?

		4	6	7
	×	8	0	0
3	7	3	6	0	0
	3	5	5	

373 600g or 373.6kg

How did I find Step 11?   ☐ Easy   ☐ OK   ☐ Difficult

Step 12: Three-digit × three-digit multiples of 10

When multiplying numbers by three-digit multiples of 10 (such as 430 or 790), split the multiple into two parts (such as 30 and 400 or 90 and 700). Multiply the parts separately and add them.

	H	T	U
	3	8	5
×	7	9	0

What to do

385 × 790 = ?

1 Split the bottom number into a multiple of 10 and a multiple of 100. Think of 790 as 90 and 700. Start by multiplying the top number by 90. Simply write a zero in the units column first and multiply the top number by 9.

	HTh	TTh	Th	H	T	U	
				3	8	5	
×				7	9	0	
			3_3	4_7	6_4	5	0	← 385 × 90

2 In the second row, multiply the top number by the **hundreds** digit. So here multiply 385 by 700. Simply write two zeros in the units and tens columns and then multiply the top number by 7.

3 Finally add your two answers. Be careful **not** to add the carry marks you used when multiplying. Just add the digits of the two answers. 34 650 + 269 500 = 304 150

	HTh	TTh	Th	H	T	U
				3	8	5
×				7	9	0
			3_3	4_7	6_4	5	0
+	2_2	6_5	9_3	5	0	0	← 385 × 700
	3	0	4	1	5	0

Now you try

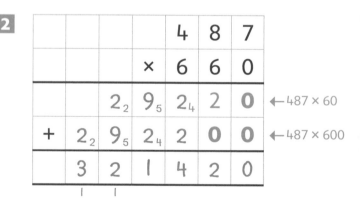

1

				4	1	3	
			×	3	5	0	
		2_2	0	6_1	5	0	←413 × 50
+	1_1	2	3	9	0	0	←413 × 300
		1	4	4	5	5	0

2

				4	8	7	
			×	6	6	0	
		2_2	9_5	2_4	2	0	←487 × 60
+	2_2	9_5	2_4	2	0	0	←487 × 600
	3	2	1	4	2	0

More practice

3

			3	4	2
		×	2	6	0
	2_2	0_2	5_1	2	0
+	6	8	4	0	0
	8	8	9	2	0

4

			5	3	9
		×	7	4	0
	2_2	1_1	5_3	6	0
+	3_3	7_2	7_6	3	0	0
	3	9	8	8	6	0

Set out these questions yourself to answer them.

5 567 × 380 = ?

HTh	TTh	Th	H	T	U
			5	6	7
		×	3	8	0
	4_4	5_5	3_5	6	0
+	1_1	7_2	0_2	1	0	0
	2	1	5	4	6	0

6 914 × 870 = ?

HTh	TTh	Th	H	T	U
			9	1	4
		×	8	7	0
	6_6	3	9_2	8	0
+	7_7	3_1	1_3	2	0	0
	7	9	5	1	8	0

Problem solving

7 A rectangular carpet has a length of 153cm and a width of 250cm. What is its area?

```
        1  5  3
    ×   2  5  0
    ─────────────
      7₂ 6₁ 5  0
  + 3₁ 0  6  0  0
    ─────────────
    3  8  2  5  0
```

38 250cm²

8 ÷ 420 = 129

Write in the missing number.

```
        1  2  9
    ×   4  2  0
    ─────────────
      2  5₁ 8  0
  + 5₁ 1₃ 6  0  0
    ─────────────
    5  4  1  8  0
```

Step 13: Multiplying two three-digit numbers
easier tables facts

Now you should be feeling confident to put it all together and multiply three-digit numbers. Simply split the bottom number into a one-digit number, a multiple of 10 and a multiple of 100 and multiply by each part separately.

	H	T	U
	2	5	1
×	2	4	3

What to do

$251 \times 243 = ?$

1 Multiply the top number by the **units** digit of the bottom number: 251×3. Remember to work from right to left and carry if necessary.

2 In the next row multiply the top number by the **tens** digit: 251×40. Simply write a zero in the units column first and multiply the top number by 4.

3 In the third row, multiply the top number by the **hundreds** digit: 251×200. Simply write two zeros in the units and tens columns and then multiply the top number by 2.

4 Finally add your three answers.

	TTh	Th	H	T	U	
			2	5	1	
×			2	4	3	
			7₁	5	3	← 251×3
	1₁	0₂	0	4	0	← 251×40
+	5₁	0	2	0	0	← 251×200
	6	0	9	9	3	

Now you try

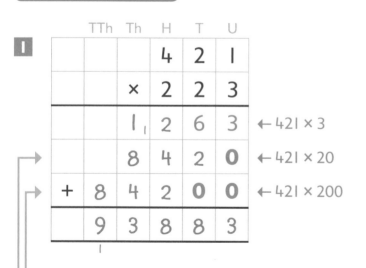

1

	TTh	Th	H	T	U	
			4	2	1	
×			2	2	3	
		1₁	2	6	3	← 421×3
		8	4	2	0	← 421×20
+	8	4	2	0	0	← 421×200
	9	3	8	8	3	

What have 421×20 and 421×200 got in common?

2

	TTh	Th	H	T	U	
			2	5	3	
×			1	4	4	
		1₁	0₂	1₁	2	← 253×4
	1₁	0₂	1₁	2	0	← 253×40
+	2	5	3	0	0	← 253×100
	3	6	4	3	2	

More practice

3

			3	2	1
		×	1	3	5
	1,	6,	0	5	
	9	6	3	0	
+	3	2	1	0	0
	4	3	3	3	5

4

			4	2	4
		×	3	3	3
	1,	2	7,	2	
	1,	2	7,	2	0
+	1,	2	7,	2	0	0
	1	4	1	1	9	2

Set out these questions yourself to answer them.

5   543 × 245 = ?

HTh	TTh	Th	H	T	U
			5	4	3
		×	2	4	5
		2₂	7₂	1₁	5
	2₂	1₁	7₁	2	0
+	1₁	0	8	6	0	0
	1	3	3	0	3	5

6   542 × 355 = ?

HTh	TTh	Th	H	T	U
			5	4	2
		×	3	5	5
		2₂	7₂	1₁	0
	2₂	7₂	1₁	0	0
+	1₁	6₁	2	6	0	0
	1	9	2	4	1	0

Problem solving

7   Find the answer to 331 × 214.

		3	3	1	
	×	2	1	4	
	1,	3,	2	4	
	3	3	1	0	
+	6	6	2	0	0
	7	0	8	3	4

70 834

8   A factory makes 621 TVs every day. How many TVs are made in 365 days?

		6	2	1	
	×	3	6	5	
	3₃	1,	0	5	
	3₃	7,	2	6	0
+	1,	8	6	3	0	0
	2	2	6	6	6	5

226 665

How did I find Step 13?	☐ Easy	☐ OK	☐ Difficult

Step 14: Multiplying two three-digit numbers
harder tables facts

These questions include harder tables facts but are done in the same way as in Step 13. Some people start with the multiple of 100. The order you multiply each part does not matter, as the final answer will be the same when you add the parts.

What to do

$879 \times 676 = ?$

1 Remember to multiply each part separately, adding zeros and carrying as necessary.

2 Add your three answers. Be careful not to add the carry marks you used when multiplying.

HTh	TTh	Th	H	T	U	
			8	7	9	
		$\times$	6	7	6	
		5_5	2_4	7_5	4	$\leftarrow 879 \times 6$
	6_6	1_5	5_6	3	0	$\leftarrow 879 \times 70$
$+$	5_5	2_4	7_5	4	0	0 $\leftarrow 879 \times 600$
	5	9	4	2	0	4

Now you try

1

			9	9	6
		$\times$	5	7	3
		2_2	9_2	8_1	8
	6_6	9_6	7_4	2	0
$+$	4_4	9_4	8_3	0	0	0
	5	7	0	7	0	8

2

			6	7	6
		$\times$	1	8	8
		5_5	4_6	0_4	8
	5_5	4_6	0_4	8	0
$+$		6	7	6	0	0
	1	2	7	0	8	8

3

			8	4	7
		$\times$	6	6	9
		7_7	6_4	2_6	3
	5_5	0_2	8_4	2	0
$+$	5_5	0_2	8_4	2	0	0
	5	6	6	6	4	3

4

			4	9	6
		$\times$	7	2	7
		3_3	4_6	7_4	2
		9_1	9_1	2	0
$+$	3_3	4_6	7_4	2	0	0
		3	6	0	5	9	2

More practice   Set out these questions yourself to answer them.

5   687 × 395 = ?

HTh	TTh	Th	H	T	U
			6	8	7
		×	3	9	5
		3_3	4_4	3_3	5
	6_6	1_7	8_6	3	0
+	2_2	0_2	6_2	1	0	0
	2	7	1	3	6	5
			1	1	

6   617 × 577 = ?

HTh	TTh	Th	H	T	U
			6	1	7
		×	5	7	7
		4_4	3_1	1_4	9
	4_4	3_1	1_4	9	0
+	3_3	0	8_3	5	0	0
	3	5	6	0	0	9
			1	1	1

Problem solving

7   Find the missing number in this division: $\boxed{272\,205}$ ÷ 345 = 789
Also write the answer in words.

```
        7 8 9
    ×   3 4 5
  ─────────────
    3₃ 9₄ 4₄ 5
  3₃ 1₃ 5₃ 6 0
+ 2₂ 3₂ 6₂ 7 0 0
  ─────────────
  2 7 2 2 0 5
    1   2   1
```

Two hundred and seventy-two thousand, two hundred and five.

8   A farmer has a field with a length of 653m and a width of 478m. What is the area of the field?

```
        6 5 3
    ×   4 7 8
  ─────────────
    5₅ 2₄ 2₂ 4
  4₄ 5₃ 7₂ 1 0
+ 2₂ 6₂ 1₁ 2 0 0
  ─────────────
  3 1 2 1 3 4
    1   1   1
```

312 134m²

How did I find Step 14?   Easy   OK   ☐ Difficult

Check-up test 3 Three-digit × three-digit

Step 11

1

			6	8	4
		×	3	0	0
2	0	5	2	0	0
	2	2	1		

2 458 × 800 = ?

			4	5	8
		×	8	0	0
3	6	6	4	0	0
	3	4	6		

Step 12

3

			4	6	6
		×	8	3	0
	1_1	3_1	9_1	8	0
+	3_3	7_5	2_4	8	0	0
	3	8	6	7	8	0
			1		

4 917 × 570 = ?

			9	1	7
		×	5	7	0
	6_6	4_1	1_4	9	0
+	4_4	5	8_3	5	0	0
	5	2	2	6	9	0
		1	1		

Steps 13 and 14

5

			4	2	6
		×	3	3	3
		1_1	2	7_1	8
	1_1	2	7_1	8	0
+	1_1	2	7_1	8	0	0
	1	4	1	8	5	8
		1	1	1	

6 687 × 862 = ?

			6	8	7
		×	8	6	2
	1_1	3_1	7_1	4
	4_4	1_5	2_4	2	0
+	5_5	4_6	9_5	6	0	0
	5	9	2	1	9	4
		1	1		

□ 1
□ 2
□ 3
□ 4
□ 5
□ 6

Steps 11 to 14 mixed

Use the grid below for working.

7 There are 586 pupils in a school. Each raises £180 for charity. How much is raised in total?

£105 480

☐ 7

8 A concert venue sells 450 tickets per performance. If there are 246 performances in a year and all the tickets are sold, how many tickets are sold in total?

110 700

☐ 8

9 A fishing boat is allowed to catch 476kg of fish per day. How many kilograms of fish is it allowed to catch each year (365 days)?

173 740kg

☐ 9

10 On a mobile phone network 412 mobiles made 306 minutes of calls each. How many minutes in total is this?

126 072 mins

☐ 10

7)

$$
\begin{array}{r}
5\ 8\ 6 \\
\times\ 1\ 8\ 0 \\
\hline
4_4\ 6_6\ 8_4\ 8\ 0 \\
+\ 5\ 8\ 6\ 0\ 0 \\
\hline
1\ 0\ 5\ 4\ 8\ 0 \\
\end{array}
$$

8)

$$
\begin{array}{r}
2\ 4\ 6 \\
\times\ 4\ 5\ 0 \\
\hline
1_1\ 2_2\ 3_3\ 0\ 0 \\
+\ 9_1\ 8_2\ 4\ 0\ 0 \\
\hline
1\ 1\ 0\ 7\ 0\ 0 \\
\end{array}
$$

9)

$$
\begin{array}{r}
4\ 7\ 6 \\
\times\ 3\ 6\ 5 \\
\hline
2_2\ 3_3\ 8_3\ 0 \\
2_2\ 8_4\ 5_3\ 6\ 0 \\
+\ 1_1\ 4_2\ 2_1\ 8\ 0\ 0 \\
\hline
1\ 7\ 3\ 7\ 4\ 0 \\
\end{array}
$$

10)

$$
\begin{array}{r}
4\ 1\ 2 \\
\times\ 3\ 0\ 6 \\
\hline
2_2\ 4\ 7_1\ 2 \\
+\ 1_1\ 2\ 3\ 6\ 0\ 0 \\
\hline
1\ 2\ 6\ 0\ 7\ 2 \\
\end{array}
$$

Total test score

☐ 10

Score	1	2	3	4	5	6	7	8	9	10
%	10	20	30	40	50	60	70	80	90	100

Step 15: Simple decimals × one-digit

Now that you can multiply whole numbers, multiplying decimals is almost as easy! All you need to do is to remember how many times smaller a decimal is than its related whole number.

$6.8 × 3$

What to do

$6.8 × 3 = ?$

1 Write the multiplication question as a new question **without** a decimal point.

$68 × 3 = ?$

2 Answer the new whole number question. $68 × 3 = 204$

3 Decide how many times smaller the decimal question is than the new whole number question. Here 6.8 is ten times smaller than 68. So the answer to the decimal question will be ten times smaller than the whole number question.

	H	T	U
		6	8
×			3
	2	0	4
		2	2

4 Finally adjust the answer so that it matches the original question. To divide a number by 10, move the digits one place to the right. To divide by 100, move the digits two places to the right.

$6.8 × 3$ is ten times smaller than $68 × 3$, so $6.8 × 3 = 20.4$

Now you try

1 $4.7 × 3 = ?$

		4	7
×			3
	1	4	1
		1	2

$4.7 × 3$ is [10] times

smaller than $47 × 3$,

so $4.7 × 3 =$ [14.1]

2 $0.35 × 5 = ?$

		3	5
×			5
	1	7	5
		1	2

$0.35 × 5$ is [100] times

smaller than $35 × 5$,

so $0.35 × 5 =$ [1.75]

3 $43 × 0.4 = ?$

		4	3
×			4
	1	7	2
		1	1

$43 × 0.4$ is [10] times

smaller than $43 × 4$,

so $43 × 0.4 =$ [17.2]

More practice   Set out these questions yourself to answer them.

4 0.36 × 6 = ?

		3	6
×			6
	2	1	6
		2	3

0.36 × 6 is [100] times

smaller than 36 × 6,

so 0.36 × 6 = [2.16]

5 9.7 × 7 = ?

		9	7
×			7
	6	7	9
		6	4

9.7 × 7 is [10] times

smaller than 97 × 7,

so 9.7 × 7 = [67.9]

6 29 × 0.8 = ?

		2	9
×			8
	2	3	2
		2	7

29 × 0.8 is [10] times

smaller than 29 × 8,

so 29 × 0.8 = [23.2]

Problem solving

7 A bottle can hold 0.7 litres of water. How many litres would 18 of these bottles hold?

	1	8
×		7
1	2	6
	1	5

18 × 0.7 is ten times smaller than 18 × 7, so 18 × 0.7 = 12.6

12.6 litres

8 A car travels 9.3km on a litre of petrol. How far will it travel on 8 litres of petrol?

	9	3
×		8
7	4	4
7	2	

9.3 × 8 is ten times smaller than 93 × 8, so 9.3 × 8 = 74.4

74.4km

9 It takes a printer 6.7 seconds to print a photo. How many seconds will it take to print five of these photos?

	6	7
×		5
3	3	5
3	3	

6.7 × 5 is ten times smaller than 67 × 5, so 6.7 × 5 = 33.5

33.5 seconds

10 Each fence panel is 0.89 metres long. How long are eight of these panels altogether?

	8	9
×		8
7	1	2
7	7	

0.89 × 8 is 100 times smaller than 89 × 8, so 0.89 × 8 = 7.12

7.12m

| **How did I find Step 15?** | ☐ Easy | ☐ OK | ☐ Difficult |

Step 16: Simple decimals × two-digit

In the same way, you can now multiply decimals using long multiplication.

7.4×34

What to do

$7.4 \times 34 = ?$

1 Write the multiplication question as a new question without a decimal point.

$74 \times 34 = ?$

2 Use the written method to answer the new whole number question. $74 \times 34 = 2516$

	Th	H	T	U	
			7	4	
×			3	4	
		2₂	9₁	6	← 74 × 4
+	2₂	2₁	2	**0**	← 74 × 30
	2	5	1	6	← 296 + 2220

3 Decide how many times smaller the decimal question is than the new whole number question. Here 7.4 is ten times smaller than 74, so the answer to the decimal question will be ten times smaller than the whole number question.

4 Finally adjust the answer so that it matches the original question. Here make 2516 ten times smaller than the whole number question. $2516 \div 10 = 251.6$

7.4 × 34 is ten times smaller than 74 × 34, so 7.4 × 34 = 251.6

Now you try

1 $4.5 \times 38 = ?$

			4	5
	×		3	8
		3₃	6₄	0
+	1₁	3₁	5	**0**
	1	7	1	0

4.5 × 38 is [10] times smaller than
45 × 38, so 4.5 × 38 = [171]

2 $0.81 \times 56 = ?$

			8	1
	×		5	6
		4₄	8	6
+	4₄	0	5	**0**
	4	5	3	6

0.81 × 56 is [100] times smaller than
81 × 56, so 0.81 × 56 = [45.36]

More practice

Set out these questions yourself to answer them.

3 $7.2 \times 63 = ?$

			7	2
	×		6	3
		2₂	1	6
+	4₄	3₁	2	0
	4	5	3	6

7.2×63 is [10] times smaller than

72×63, so $7.2 \times 63 =$ [453.6]

4 $27 \times 8.4 = ?$

			2	7
	×		8	4
		1₁	0₂	8
+	2₂	1₅	6	0
	2	2	6	8

27×8.4 is [10] times smaller than

27×84, so $27 \times 8.4 =$ [226.8]

Problem solving

5 $71 \times 6.6 = ?$

			7	1
	×		6	6
		4₄	2	6
+	4₄	2	6	0
	4	6	8	6

71×6.6 is [10] times smaller than

71×66, so $71 \times 6.6 =$ [468.6]

6 $2.03 \times 43 = ?$

		2	0	3
	×		4	3
		6	0	9
+	8	1₁	2	0
	8	7	2	9

2.03×43 is [100] times smaller than

203×43, so $2.03 \times 43 =$ [87.29]

| **How did I find Step 16?** | ☐ Easy | ☐ OK | ☐ Difficult |

Step 17: Multiplying two decimals **with one decimal place**

When multiplying two decimals together, adjust the answer in the same way. For example, 5.1×3.6 is 100 times smaller than 51×36. So you find the answer to 51×36 and then divide by 100.

$$5.1 \times 3.6$$

What to do

$$5.1 \times 3.6 = ?$$

1 Write the question without the decimal points.

$$51 \times 36 = ?$$

2 Answer the new whole number question.

3 Decide how many times smaller the original question is and adjust the answer.

	Th	H	T	U
			5	1
×			3	6
		3_3	0	6
+	1_1	5	3	**0**
	1	8	3	6

4 A useful way to check if you have put the decimal point in the correct place is to count up the number of digits after the decimal points in the question and then check that the same number of digits are after the decimal point in the answer: $5.\underline{1} \times 3.\underline{6} = 18.\underline{36}$

5.1×3.6 is 100 times smaller than 51×36, so $5.1 \times 3.6 = 18.36$

Now you try

1 $2.5 \times 5.6 = ?$

			2	5
	×		5	6
		1	5_3	0
+	1_1	2_2	5	0
	1	4	0	0
		1		

2.5×5.6 is ☐ 100 ☐ times smaller than 25×56, so $2.5 \times 5.6 = $ ☐ 14.00 or 14 ☐

2 $3.2 \times 9.8 = ?$

			3	2
	×		9	8
		2_2	5_1	6
+	2_2	8_1	8	0
	3	1	3	6
		1	1	

3.2×9.8 is ☐ 100 ☐ times smaller than 32×98, so $3.2 \times 9.8 = $ ☐ 31.36 ☐

More practice

Set out these questions yourself to answer them.

3 8.1 × 3.7 = ?

Th	H	T	U
		8	1
×		3	7
	5₅	6	7
+	2₂	4	3	0
	2	9	9	7

8.1 × 3.7 is 100 times smaller than

81 × 37, so 8.1 × 3.7 = 29.97

4 7.6 × 4.3 = ?

Th	H	T	U
		7	6
×		4	3
	2₂	2₁	8
+	3₃	0₂	4	0
	3	2	6	8

7.6 × 4.3 is 100 times smaller than

76 × 43, so 7.6 × 4.3 = 32.68

Problem solving

5 Find the product of
6.3 and 3.9.

```
        6   3
    ×   3   9
    5₅  6₂  7
+  1₁  8   9   0
    2   4   5   7
        ₁       ₁
```

6.3 × 3.9 is 100 times
smaller than 63 × 39,
so 6.3 × 3.9 = 24.57

24.57

6 A rug has a length of
4.3m and a width of 2.8m.
What is the area of the rug?

```
        4   3
    ×   2   8
    3₃  4₂  4
+       8   6   0
    1   2   0   4
        ₁       ₁
```

4.3 × 2.8 is 100 times
smaller than 43 × 28,
so 4.3 × 2.8 = 12.04

12.04m²

| **How did I find Step 17?** | Easy | OK | ☐ Difficult |

Step 18: Multiplying two decimals with one or two decimal places

Well done – you are at the last step! These questions are similar to the last few steps, but sometimes may involve numbers that are 1000 times smaller than the whole number questions, for example 9.84×7.3 is 1000 times smaller than 984×73.

9.84×7.3

What to do

$9.84 \times 7.3 = ?$

1 Write the question without the decimal points.

$984 \times 73 = ?$

2 Answer the whole number question.

3 Decide how many times smaller the original question is and adjust the answer.

4 Count up the number of digits after the decimal points in the question and check that the answer has the same number: $9.\underline{84} \times 7.\underline{3} = 71.\underline{832}$

		TTh	Th	H	T	U
				9	8	4
			×		7	3
			2_2	9_2	5_1	2
	+	6_6	8_5	8_2	8	0
		7	1	8	3	2
			1	1	1	

9.84×7.3 is 1000 times smaller than 984×73, so $9.84 \times 7.3 = 71.832$

Now you try

1 $1.24 \times 5.6 = ?$

		1	2	4
	×		5	6
		7_1	4_2	4
+	6_1	2_2	0	0
	6	9	4	4

1.24×5.6 is [1000] times smaller than 124×56, so $1.24 \times 5.6 =$ [6.944]

2 $3.35 \times 9.8 = ?$

		3	3	5
	×		9	8
	2_2	6_2	8_4	0
+	3_3	0_3	1_4	5	0
	3	2	8	3	0
		1			

3.35×9.8 is [1000] times smaller than 335×98, so $3.35 \times 9.8 =$ [32.830 or 32.83]

More practice

Write the missing decimal in each question using these whole number calculations to help.

			5	7	6
		×		4	6
		3_3	4_4	5_3	6
+	2_2	3_3	0_2	4	0
	2	6	4	9	6

			7	1	7
		×		8	9
		6_6	4_1	5_6	3
+	5_5	7_1	3_5	6	0
	6	3	8	1	3

3 $5.76 \times \boxed{4.6} = 26.496$

4 $\boxed{7.17} \times 8.9 = 63.813$

5 $57.6 \times \boxed{4.6} = 264.96$

6 $\boxed{71.7} \times 8.9 = 638.13$

7 $576 \times \boxed{4.6} = 2649.6$

8 $\boxed{71.7} \times 89 = 6381.3$

Problem solving

9 Which is larger: 57.8×4.6 or 6.78×3.9?

57.8 × 4.6, as 265.88

is larger than 26.442

			5	7	8
		×		4	6
		3_3	4_4	6_4	8
+	2_2	3_3	1_3	2	0
	2	6	5	8	8

			6	7	8
		×		3	9
		6_6	1_7	0_7	2
+	2_2	0_2	3_2	4	0
	2	6	4	4	2

10 What is 3.33×3.3?

			3	3	3
		×		3	3
			9	9	9
+		9	9	9	0
1	0	9	8	9	

10.989

11 What is 6.66×6.6?

			6	6	6
		×		6	6
		3_3	9_3	9_3	6
+	3_3	9_3	9_3	6	0
	4	3	9	5	6

43.956

| **How did I find Step 18?** | Easy | OK | ☐ Difficult |

Final test Long multiplication of whole numbers and decimals

Steps 15 to 18

1 $2.7 \times 6 = ?$

		2	7
×			6
	1	6	2
		1	4

2.7×6 is [10] times smaller than 27×6,

so $2.7 \times 6 =$ [16.2]

2 $0.38 \times 5 = ?$

		3	8
×			5
	1	9	0
		1	4

0.38×5 is [100] times smaller than 38×5,

so $0.38 \times 5 =$ [1.90 or 1.9]

$\square_1$
$\square_2$

3 $27 \times 2.6 = ?$

			2	7
	×		2	6
		1₁	6₄	2
+		5₁	4	0
		7	0	2

27×2.6 is [10] times smaller than 27×26,

so $27 \times 2.6 =$ [70.2]

4 $8.35 \times 6.1 = ?$

			8	3	5
		×		6	1
			8	3	5
+	5₅	0₂	1₃	0	0
	5	0	9	3	5

8.35×6.1 is [1000] times smaller than 835×61,

so $8.35 \times 6.1 =$ [50.935]

$\square_3$
$\square_4$

Steps 1 to 18 mixed

Use spare paper for working.

5 Find the product of 5137 and 20.

102 740

☐ 5

6 A cinema has 66 seats in each row. If there are 38 rows, how many seats are there in total?

2508

☐ 6

7 There are 16 biscuits in each pack. How many biscuits are there in 86 packs?

1376

☐ 7

8 Chloe runs on 143 days. If each run is 13km, how far does she run in total?

1859km

☐ 8

9 How many hours are there in 365 days?

8760 hours

☐ 9

10 What is 444 × 44?

19 536

☐ 10

11 A plane travels an average of 756km each day for 230 days a year. How many kilometres is this?

173 880km

☐ 11

12 A farmer has a field with a length of 654m and a width of 448m. What is the area of the field?

292 992m²

☐ 12

13 Find the product of 3.62 and 3.1.

11.222

☐ 13

14 A shop sold 37 computers in one month. Each computer sold for £389. How much did the shop get for them?

£14 393

☐ 14

15 What is 637 × 588?

374 556

☐ 15

16 What is 5.55 × 5.5?

30.525

☐ 16

Total test score

Score	1	2	3	4	5	6	7	8	9	10	11	12	13	14	15	16
%	6	13	19	25	31	38	44	50	56	63	69	75	81	88	94	100

16

Written Calculation

Group record sheet

Pupil Book: _____

Class/Set: _____

Pupil's name	Check-up test 1	Check-up test 2	Check-up test 3	Final test	Assessment test 1*	Assessment test 2*	Mixed calculations test*

*Available as assessment resources in the back of the **Written Calculation: Teacher's Guide** (ISBN 978 07217 1278 9)

From: **Written Calculation: Multiplication 2 Answers** by Hilary Koll and Steve Mills (ISBN 978 07217 1275 8). Copyright © Schofield & Sims Ltd, 2015. Published by Schofield & Sims Ltd, Dogley Mill, Fenay Bridge, Huddersfield HD8 0NQ, UK (www.schofieldandsims.co.uk). This page may be photocopied after purchase for use within your school or institution only.